Helpful Harry

Susannah McFarlane   Lachlan Creagh

A Scholastic Australia Book

This is Harry, and some of his friends Henrietta, Hamish, Hannah and Holden.

Harry is helpful. He is one of the most helpful blue heelers in all the high hills.

Helping is Harry's hobby. He is happiest when he is lending a hand.

He helps Helga, the hen, hang a hatstand for her hatchlings.

He hastily helps Holden herd the
hungry heifers to their hay.

He helps hysterical honey-eaters
hunt for honey.

Then one day, there was a humungous hullabaloo. The heavy metal hawks were having their half-year hoedown. But Harrison, the handsome host, couldn't find his harmonica.

No harmonica, no hoedown!
How hopeless!

Harry heard about the harmonica hiccup and hurried to the hoedown. It was haywire! The hawks were **heartbroken**.

'I'll help,' said Harry. 'We heelers
are hugely into hunting.'

So Harry, Henrietta, Hamish, Hannah
and Holden started to hunt.

They hunted under hats, in haysheds
and hutches and even in hot dogs.

They hunted on house boats, around clothes hoists and in hen houses (luckily Helga wasn't home).

Harry hunted and hunted, until he had a hunch . . . Hurrah!

The harmonica! It was hidden under a hydrangea!

'Hip hip hooray for Harry,' howled the hawks as the heavy metal hoedown heated up again. 'Harry, you're our hero! Thanks heaps for helping us!'

Good on you Harry
(and Hamish,
Hannah, Henrietta
and Holden).

What about you?
Are you helpful too?